Mr. PANtS

IT'S GO TIME!

WORDS BY
SCOTT McCORMICK ...ELL

SCHOLASTIC INC.

TO SOEN AND SADIE, THE COOLEST CATS I KNOW
"ALL . . ."   —S.M.

FOR MY PARENTS, CAROLE AND BOB
—R.H.L.

ISBN 978-0-545-83945-7

Text copyright © 2014 by Scott McCormick. Pictures copyright © 2014 by R. H. Lazzell. All rights reserved.
Published by Scholastic Inc., 557 Broadway, New York, NY 10012, by arrangement with Dial Books for Young Readers,
a division of Penguin Young Readers Group, a member of Penguin Group (USA) LLC, A Penguin Random House
Company. SCHOLASTIC and associated logos are trademarks and/or registered trademarks of Scholastic Inc.

12 11 10 9 8 7 6 5 4 3 2 1   15 16 17 18 19 20/0

Printed in the U.S.A.   40

First Scholastic printing, January 2015

Designed by Jennifer Kelly
Text set in Archer

CONTENTS

HA HA HA HO
HA HEE
HO HA
HEE

4

8

15

I'M GOING TO LASER TAG!

I'M GOING TO LASER TAG!

22

Chapter Two:
BOXY

29

33

34

35

43

46

Chapter Th[ree]
PRINCESS PA[RTY]

It's Princess-TASTIC!

Why are we doing this?

49

Grommy wanted to do something special with you and Foot Foot on the last day of summer.

Come on, Mr. Pants. It'll be fun!

Fairy Princess Dream Factory

WELCOME!

The Fairy Princess Dream Factory? That's the opposite of fun!

Heads

Dresses

Wands

Jewelry

Wigs

Scarves

Hello and welcome to the Fairy Princess Dream Factory, where all your fairy princess dreams can come true!

54

58

Chapter Four:
IT'S GO TIME

So, after shopping we can do laser tag?

It's already pretty late, but I'll tell you what: If we get done shopping by five thirty, we can do laser tag. Otherwise we have to go home. Okay?

Five thirty? Okay. What do we need from the store?

Ten minutes later . . .

WE STAB HIGH PRICES!

Okay, last stop. Shoes.

77

81

Chapter Five:
A TREAT FOR FEET

LOOSTNER'S

LASER TAG

Settle down,
Mr. Pants.

Laser tag!

Laser tag!

Laser tag!

90

Hey!
This is fun!
Did you know Mom could do that?
Look, we've got to be smart here. Let's go after . . .
VEST ON!
YOU'VE BEEN HIT!

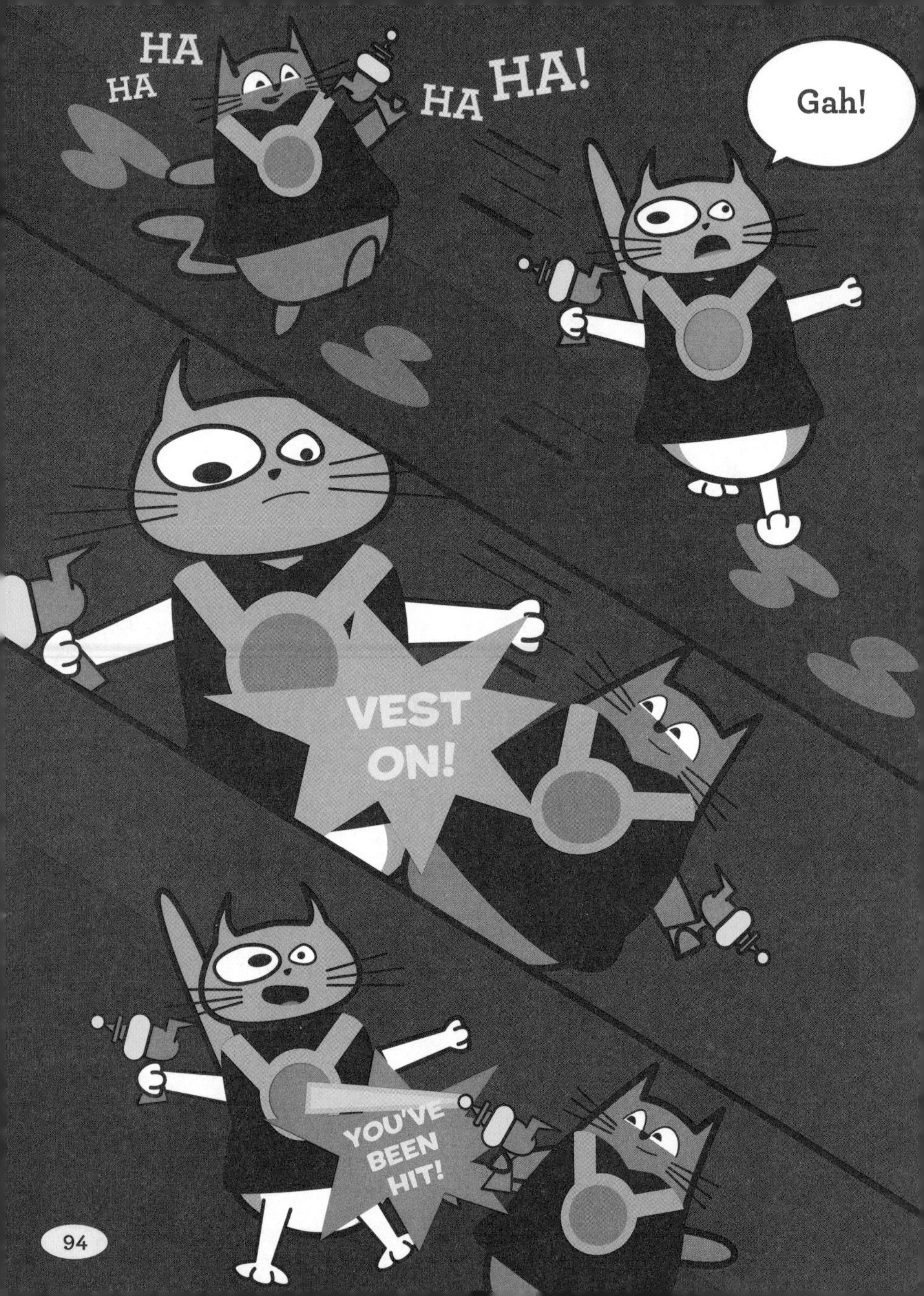
HA HA
HA HA!
Gah!
VEST ON!
YOU'VE BEEN HIT!

95

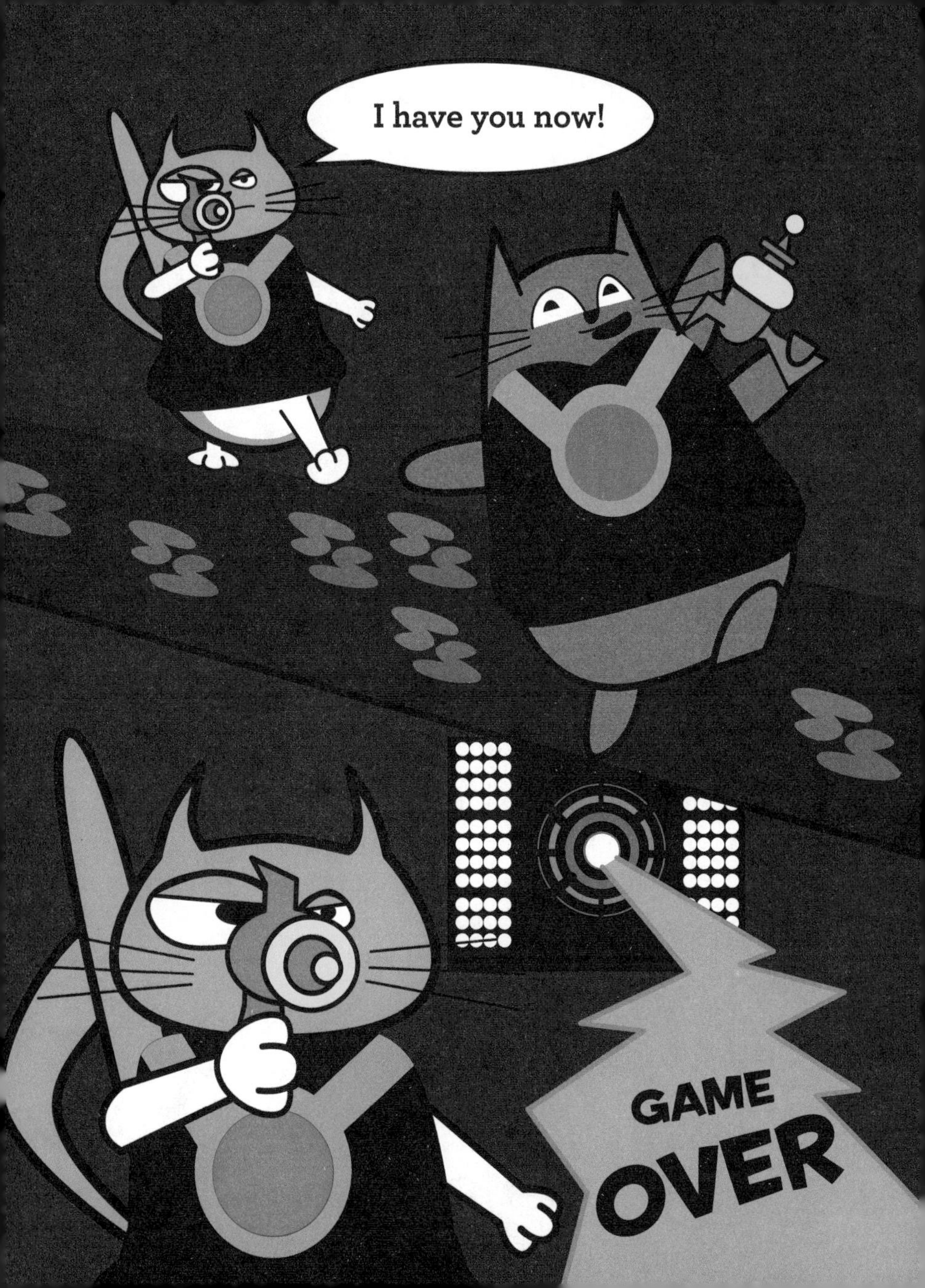
I have you now!
GAME
OVER

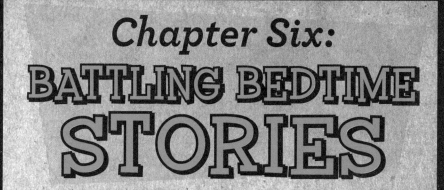

Chapter Six:
BATTLING BEDTIME STORIES

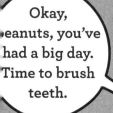

Okay, peanuts, you've had a big day. Time to brush teeth.

But I didn't get to play with my wombat!

I got a rainbow unicorn backpack!

I'm gonna miss Mr. Pants and Foot Foot!

Yeah, yeah, yeah. Teeth time.

106

117

Chapter Seven:
WUB-BY!
WUB-BY! WUB-BY!

SUMMER SCHMUMMER!
WELCOME BACK TO SCHOOL!

Room 237

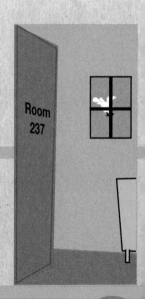